W9-CFP-710

Number Games

Grade **K**

This book belongs to:

_____

Printed in China

Tasty Pizza

Daniel has bought **3** slices of pizza. Colour the pizza he has.

Where Is It?

Sam is looking for the baseball. Colour the path with **2** bats.

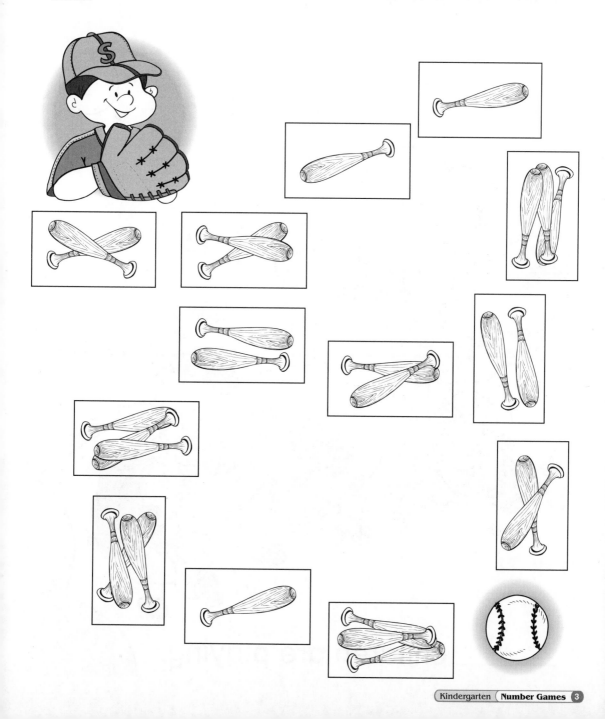

In the Park

Four children are in the park. Count and write how many children are playing.

_____ children are playing.

In the Bakery

Mom has bought some food for breakfast. Count and draw lines to match.

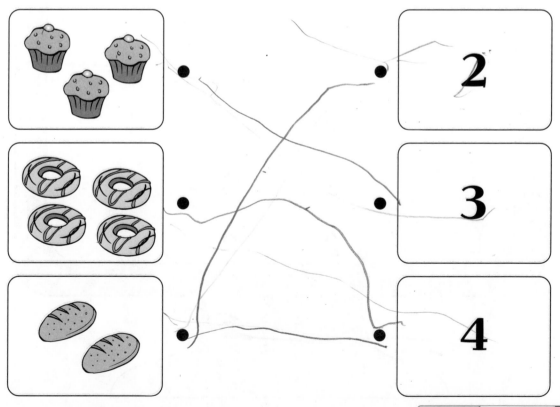

2

3

4

Is It a House?

Bill is drawing on his computer. Count and circle the correct numbers.

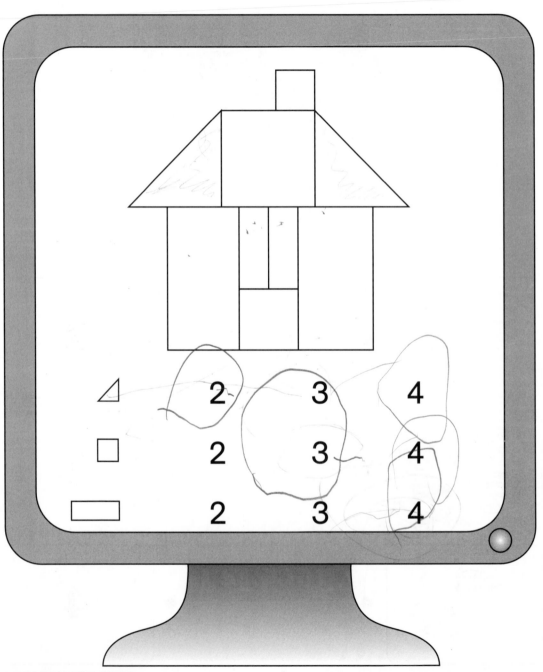

2   3   4

2   3   4

2   3   4

Bill's Aquarium

Bill has some goldfish. Count and write how many goldfish he has.

Bill has _____ goldfish.

In the Gym

The basketball players are lining up in the gym. Write the missing numbers on their vests.

Mike's Caps

Mike has **4** caps in his wardrobe. Draw the missing caps.

Good Habit

Shirley and Daisy have saved some coins. Count and circle the correct answer.

Who has more coins?

Playing with Blocks

Alan has made a train with blocks. Count and circle the correct numbers. Colour the train.

	1	2	3
△	1	2	3
▭	2	3	4
▢	3	4	5
○	3	4	5

Happy Birthday

Ada is 5 years old. Draw 5 candles on her birthday cake.
Colour the cake.

Merry Christmas

Paul has put his presents under the Christmas tree. Count and write how many presents he has got.

Paul has got _____ presents.

Get Set!

Some race cars do not have a number. Write the missing numbers. Colour the cars.

START

1

3

4

Shopping for Fruits

How many fruits did Mom buy? Count and draw lines to match.

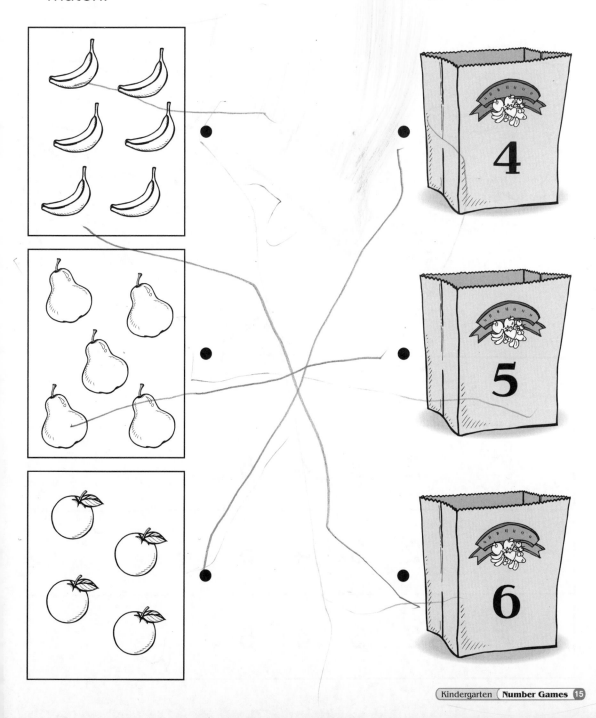

Up in the Sky

There are many kites in the sky. Count and circle the correct answers.

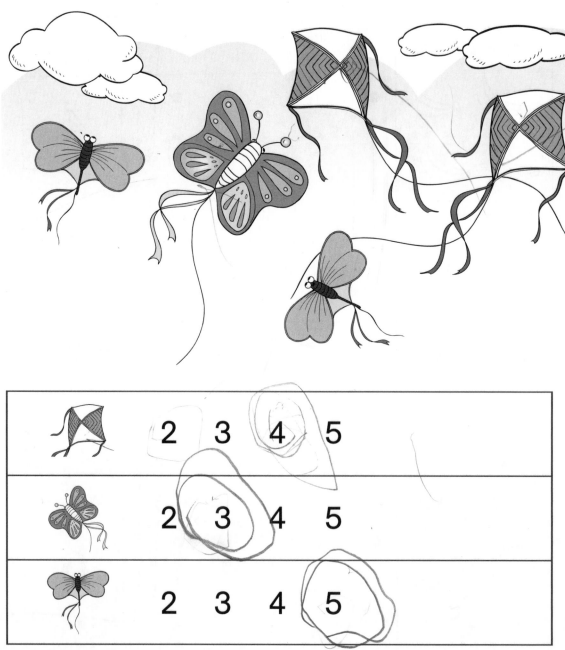

	2	3	4	5
	2	3	4	5
	2	3	4	5

   is the most in number.

Funny Cartoons

Mary is watching cartoons on the couch. How long is the couch? Count the  and write the correct number.

The couch is about _____ long.

Happy Easter

Eric has **6** Easter eggs. Draw the missing eggs in the basket. Colour the eggs.

In the Circus

The clown and the animals are playing tricks. Which shape is the most in number? Colour the correct answer.

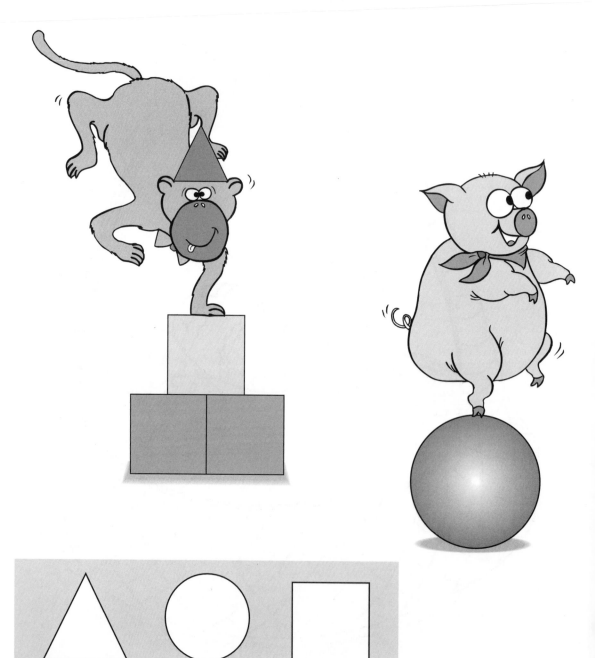

The Carnival

The booths are decorated with balloons. Colour the booth with **7** balloons.

Piggy Banks

Daniel saves his coins in the piggy banks. Count the coins and draw lines to match.

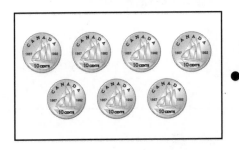

Bill's Toy Cars

Bill has many toy cars. Count and circle the correct numbers.

🚌	3	4	5
🚚	4	5	6
🚗	5	6	7

In the Bathroom

There is a mat on the floor. Count the  and write the correct number. Colour the mat.

The mat is about _____ long.

Up the Stairs

Sam is going up to his bedroom. Write the missing numbers on the stairs.

On the Beach

Daisy and Mary are collecting shells on the beach. Colour the box with **8** shells.

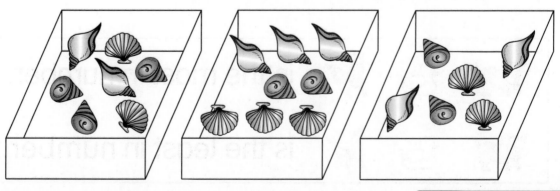

A Beautiful Park

There are many lovely animals and insects in the park.
Count and circle the correct answers.

   is the most in number.

   is the least in number.

A Barbecue

Daniel is cooking meat for his friends. Count and draw lines to match.

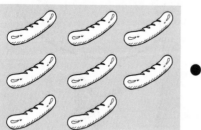 

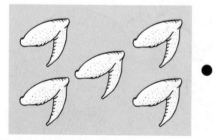 

A Good Harvest

Ada is picking apples in an orchard. Count and write how many apples there are in the basket.

There are _____ apples in the basket.

On the Baseball Field

The children have left their things on the field after the game. Count and circle the correct numbers.

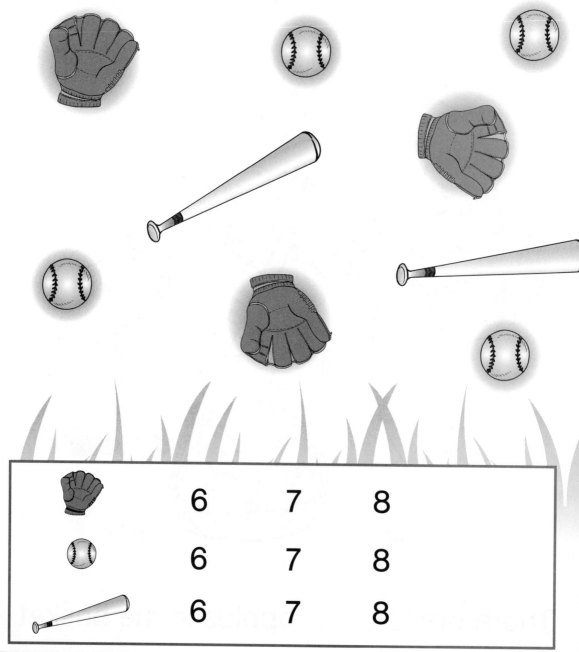

	6	7	8
	6	7	8
	6	7	8

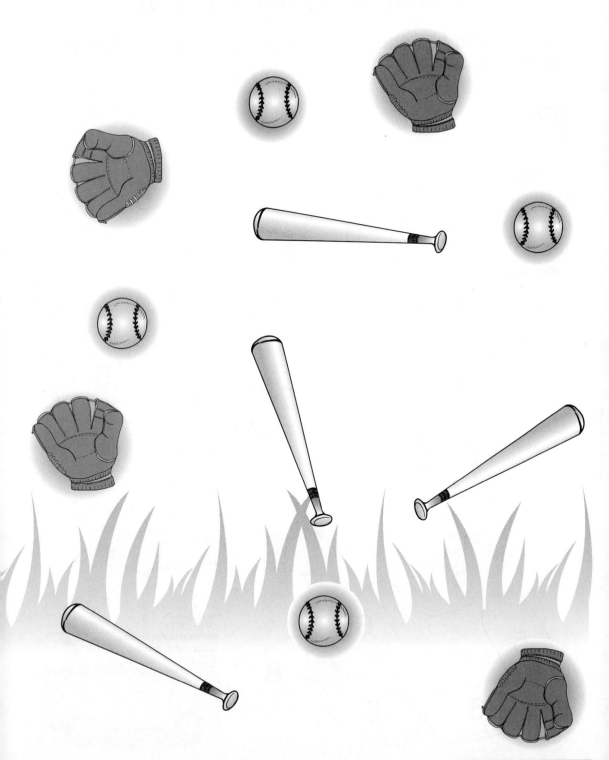

A Hot Dog for Lunch

Help Jason find the way to buy a hot dog. Colour the path from **2** to **8**.

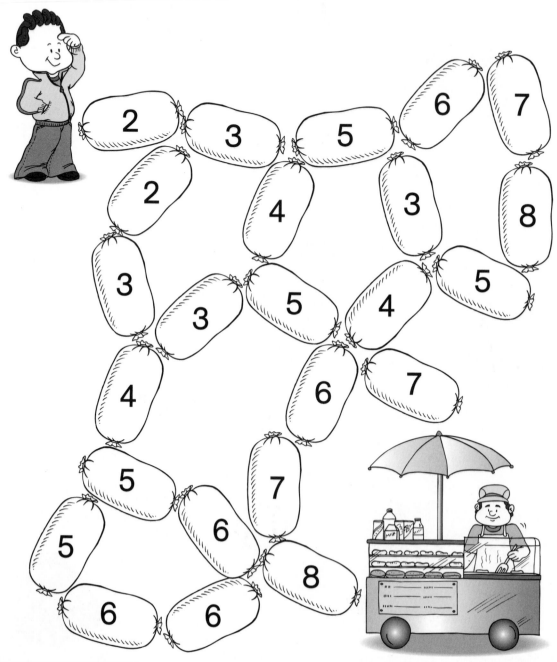

A Tricky Toss

The clown is tossing some balls. Draw more balls to make it **8**.

Blowing Bubbles

Scott and Mike are blowing bubbles. Put a ☑ to show who blows more bubbles.

Lucky Draw

Susan has drawn the smallest number. Which is Susan's prize? Colour it.

 8

 3

 6

Magic Time

The magician is taking a strip of flowers out of his hat.
Write the missing numbers.

Shopping Fun

There are many toys in the toy shop. Count and circle the correct numbers.

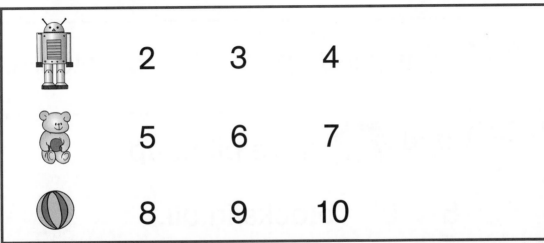

Building Towers

Matthew and Robin are building towers with some blocks.
Count and circle the correct numbers.

 has piled up 4 5 6 blocks.

 has piled up 4 5 6 blocks.

 and have piled up

7 8 9 blocks in all.

Mr. Smith's Sheep

Mr. Smith has some sheep on his farm. Count and write how many sheep there are.

There are _____ sheep.

Sam's Phone

Look at Sam's phone. Write the missing numbers.

Who Has More?

Shirley and Jenny have collected many stickers. Put a ✔
to show who has more.

Ada's Candies

Help Ada put the candies into the right jars. Count and draw lines to match.

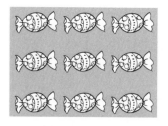 •   •

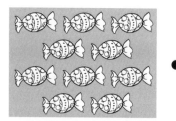 •   •

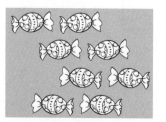 •   •

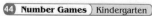

Reading Time

The children are reading on the carpet. How long is the carpet? Count the  and write the correct number.

The carpet is about _____  long.

On the Lake

There are many sailboats on the lake. Count and circle the correct number.

There are   9   10   11   sailboats on the lake.

The Busy Postman

The postman wants to deliver a letter to Mr. Brown. Colour his path from the smallest to the biggest number.

Beautiful Beads

Lisa has different beads. Which two are the same in number? Colour them.

On the Platform

Look out! A train is arriving. Write the missing numbers.

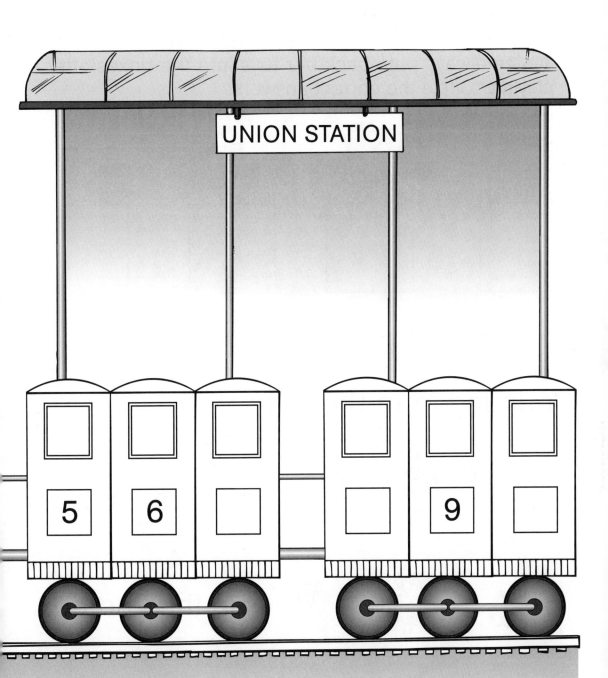

UNION STATION

5 6

9

Janice's Toys

Janice always puts back her toys into the boxes after playing. Circle the correct answers.

  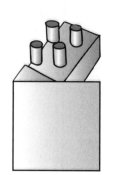 

Counting from the left :

    is in the 1st box.

    is in the 2nd box.

    is in the 3rd box.

Going to the Zoo

The children are lining up at the entrance. Circle the correct answers.

Who is 1st?

Who is 2nd?

Who is 3rd?

The Pet Shop

The pets are lovely. Count and circle the correct numbers.

🐶	2	3	4
🐱	2	3	4

There are   9   10   11   pets in all.

Time to Get Up

It is time to get up. Write the missing numbers on the clock face.

Great Job Award

_____

has successfully completed
this activity book

Signed: _____

Date: _____